GARFIELD
Going for Gold

JIM DAVIS

ℛℛ
RAVETTE PUBLISHING

First published by Ravette Publishing 2012.

Printed and bound by CPI Group (UK) Ltd,
Croydon, CR0 4YY
for Ravette Publishing Limited,
PO Box 876
Horsham
West Sussex RH12 9GH

ISBN: 978-1-84161-364-2

JIM DAVIS 7-29

JIM DAVIS 8-19

www.garfield.com

JIM DAVIS 7-22

OTHER GARFIELD BOOKS AVAILABLE

Pocket Books	Price	ISBN
Am I Bothered?	£3.99	978-1-84161-286-7
Don't Ask!	£3.99	978-1-84161-247-8
Feed Me!	£3.99	978-1-84161-242-3
Gooooal!	£3.99	978-1-84161-329-1
Gotcha!	£3.50	978-1-84161-226-3
I Am What I Am!	£3.99	978-1-84161-243-0
Kowabunga	£3.99	978-1-84161-246-1
Numero Uno	£3.99	978-1-84161-297-3
S.W.A.L.K.	£3.50	978-1-84161-225-6
Talk to the Paw	£3.99	978-1-84161-317-8
Time to Delegate	£3.99	978-1-84161-296-6
Wan2tlk?	£3.99	978-1-84161-264-5
Wassup?	£3.99	978-1-84161-355-0
Whatever!	£3.99	978-1-84161-330-7

Classics		
Volume One	£7.99	978-1-85304-970-5
Volume Two	£7.99	978-1-85304-971-2
Volume Three	£7.99	978-1-85304-996-5
Volume Four	£7.99	978-1-85304-997-2
Volume Five	£7.99	978-1-84161-022-1
Volume Six	£7.99	978-1-84161-023-8
Volume Seven	£7.99	978-1-84161-088-7
Volume Eight	£7.99	978-1-84161-089-4
Volume Nine	£7.99	978-1-84161-149-5
Volume Ten	£7.99	978-1-84161-150-1
Volume Eleven	£7.99	978-1-84161-175-4
Volume Twelve	£7.99	978-1-84161-176-1
Volume Thirteen	£7.99	978-1-84161-206-5
Volume Fourteen	£7.99	978-1-84161-207-2
Volume Fifteen	£5.99	978-1-84161-232-4
Volume Sixteen	£5.99	978-1-84161-233-1
Volume Seventeen	£7.99	978-1-84161-250-8
Volume Eighteen	£6.99	978-1-84161 251-5
Volume Nineteen	£6.99	978-1-84161-303-1
Volume Twenty	£6.99	978-1-84161 304-8
Volume Twenty One	£7.99	978-1-84161-359-8

Miscellaneous		
Colour Collection Book 3	£11.99	978-1-84161-320-8
Colour Collection Book 2	£10.99	978-1-84161-306-2
Colour Collection Book 1	£10.99	978-1-84161-293-5